the NIGHT before Christmas

Written by **Oliver Lancaster**

Illustrated by **Hannah Green**

'Twas the night before Christmas

When all through the stable

Every creature was stirring

This ain't a fable!

No stockings were hung
No chimney in sight

But one thing's for sure
The Lord came that night!

Visions of angels
Thronged overhead.

singing

It's written
in this book!

HOLY
BIBLE

So upwards they looked
To witness the clatter

And jumped to their feet
To see what was the matter.

On hearing the news
They flew like a flash
Although in flip-flops,
So... not quite a dash!

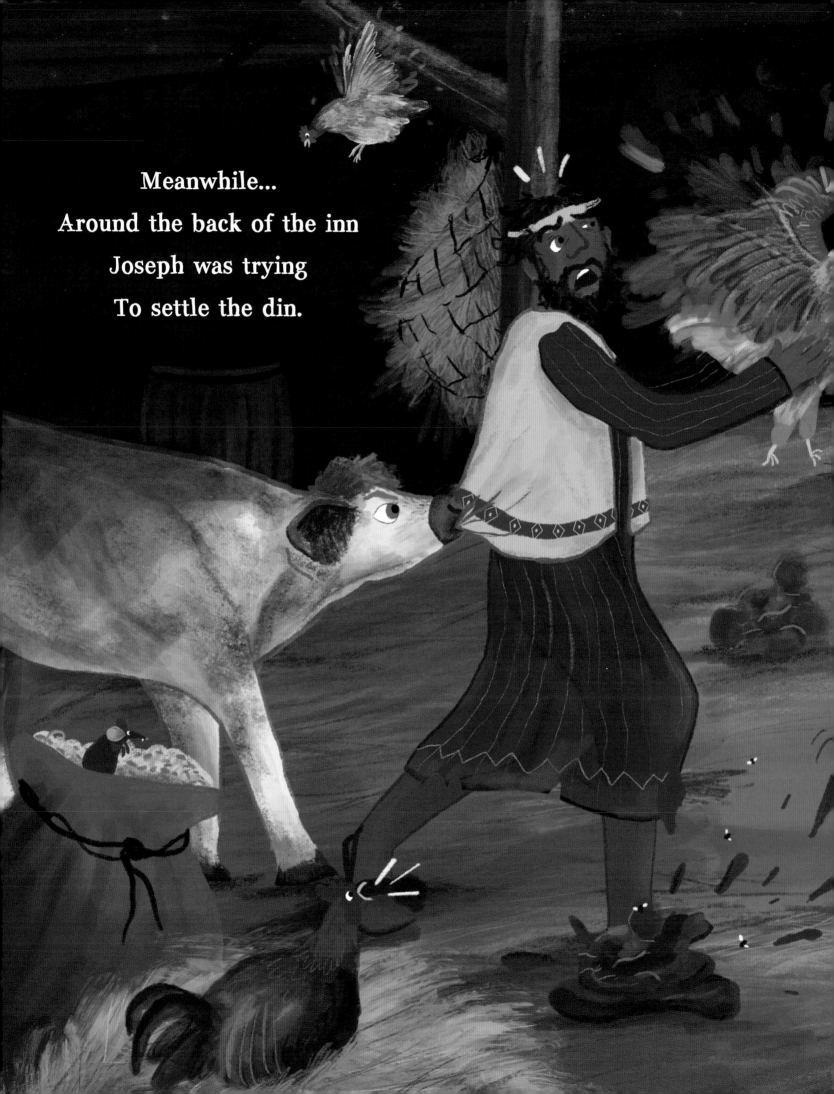

Meanwhile...
Around the back of the inn
Joseph was trying
To settle the din.

The cattle were lowing
Or was it a moo?

Either way,
There was lots of ... mess!

Anyway, Mary was tired
And needed to lay

So Joseph made her
A bed out of hay.

And just before the baby came
(Yes, he nearly forgot)

He set up a manger
Because there wasn't a cot.

Now off in the east
There were some wise guys
Who were studying hard
And pointing up to the skies.

When what to their wondering
eyes should appear?

But a big sparkly star,
A special sign,
So clear!

Merrily on high!
And with a

DONG

and a **DING**

They knew in a moment
There was a new born king.

Not quite rapid eagles,
Their camels they came

Loaded up with gifts

They checked them by name:

Then off to deliver them
To the child foretold.

Back to the stable
And at long last
All the prophecies
Had come to pass.

BETHLEHEM

The waiting was over.

He was finally here.

Jesus our
Saviour.

Holy. Near.

The shepherds arrived,

Their jolly good selves

But there was no sleigh full of toys
And no hard-working elves.

And then the wise men came...

A bit late... but to bring   Their precious gifts
To the treasured King.

There were no Christmas dinners,
No Pop Factor winners,
Nothing on the telly,
No bowls full of jelly.

But now, I hope,
You will have heard and read

DAVID

BOAZ

That when believing in Jesus
You have nothing to dread.

ABRAHAM

Because, on that first day of Christmas,
From Abraham's family tree,

Came God's Son,

JESUS
CHRIST

The Greatest Gift - born to set us free!

So... tonight, beneath the stars so bright,
With snow outside (perhaps, sparkling white?)
Merry Christmas to all
And to all a good night!

ISBN: 978-1-915705-01-3

Published by 10Publishing, a division of 10ofThose Limited,
Tomlinson Road, Leyland, Lancs, PR25 2DY, England

info@10ofthose.com
www.10ofthose.com

Written by Oliver Lancaster
Illustrated by Hannah Green
Designed by Diane Warnes

1 3 5 7 10 8 6 4 2

'I dedicate this book to my creative little family; to my creative northern nurturers in theatre and education; to my creative, liberating spoken word-on-the-street influence; to my church for a lot of creative freedom; and above all, to my creator, saviour and comforter.' OL

'For my husband Tom, a constant help and who always inspires.' HG

10Publishing is committed to publishing quality Christian resources that are biblical, accessible and point people to Jesus.

www.10ofthose.com is our online retail partner
selling thousands of quality books at discounted prices.

For information contact: info@10ofthose.com
or check out our website: www.10ofthose.com